What colour is the fluffy chick?

It's a chick!
The egg goes crrr-ack.

kitten

Little **kittens** run and bounce.

They love to play and chase and pounce!

baby elephant

Baby **elephant**,
stretch your trunk.

Hold on tight now,
trumpety trump!

piglet

Piglets, give your tails a wiggle.

Watch those curly
tails wriggle!

baby bird

One, two, three, four
birds I see...

High up, nesting
in their tree.

calf

Who's this baby,
black and white?

What is the mummy animal called?

If you said **calf** then you were right!

cub

Little **lion** cubs
love to play.

Can you roar like a little lion cub?

They practise doing roars all day.

lamb

Lambs like to skip and jump around.

They leap up high
above the ground.

puppy

Happy **puppies** love the park.

See their tails wag.
Hear them bark.

foal

Be careful, little **foal**, don't fall.

Straighten your legs
and stand up tall!

mouse

Point to the mouse's wiggly tail.

Here's a tiny baby **mouse**.
Can you see his tiny house?